Grade 3 Level 3 Late elementary **Piano**

Improve your sight-reading!

Paul Harris

FABER _ff_ MUSIC

Practice chart

	Comments (from you, your teacher or parent)	*Done!*
Stage 1		
Stage 2		
Stage 3		
Stage 4		
Stage 5		
Stage 6		
Stage 7		
Stage 8		
Stage 9		

Teacher's name _____

Telephone _____

Many thanks to Jean Cockburn, Claire Dunham, Graeme Humphrey and Diana Jackson for their invaluable help, and particular thanks to Lesley Rutherford whose editorial skills and perpetual encouragement went far beyond the call of duty.

© 2008 by Faber Music Ltd.
This edition first published in 2008 by Faber Music Ltd.
Bloomsbury House, 74–77 Great Russell Street, London WC1B 3DA
Music setting by Graham Pike
Cover and page design by Susan Clarke
Cover illustration by Drew Hillier
Printed in England by Caligraving Ltd
All rights reserved

ISBN10: 0-571-53303-5 (US edition 0-571-53313-2)
EAN13: 978-0-571-53303-9 (US edition 978-0-571-53313-8)

To buy Faber Music publications or to find out about the full range of titles available
please contact your local music retailer or Faber Music sales enquiries:
Faber Music Ltd, Burnt Mill, Elizabeth Way, Harlow CM20 2HX
Tel: +44 (0) 1279 82 89 82   Fax: +44 (0) 1279 82 89 83
sales@fabermusic.com   fabermusic.com

Introduction

Being a good sight-reader is so important and it needn't be difficult! If you work through this book carefully – always making sure that you really understand each exercise before you play it you'll never have problems learning new pieces or doing well at sight-reading in exams!

Using the workbook

1 Rhythmic exercises

Make sure you have grasped these fully before you go on to the melodic exercises: it is vital that you really know how the rhythms work. There are a number of ways to do the exercises – see *Improve your sight-reading* Grade 1 for more details.

2 Melodic exercises

These exercises use just the notes and rhythms for the Stage, and also give some help with fingering. If you want to sight-read fluently and accurately, get into the habit of working through each exercise in the following ways before you begin to play it:

- Make sure you understand the rhythm and counting. Clap the exercise through.
- Look at the shape of the tune, particularly the highest and lowest notes. Which finger do you need to start on to be able to play it? The exercises have this fingering added to get you started.
- Try to hear the piece through in your head. Always play the first note to help.

3 Prepared pieces

Work your way through the questions first, as these will help you to think about or 'prepare' the piece. Don't begin playing until you are pretty sure you know exactly how the piece goes.

4 Going solo!

It is now up to you to discover the clues in this series of practice pieces. Give yourself about a minute and do your best to understand the piece before you play. Check the rhythms and hand position, and try to hear the piece in your head.

Always remember to feel the pulse and to keep going steadily once you've begun. Good luck and happy sight-reading!

Terminology:
Bar = measure

Stage 1

The examples in earlier books have all remained in a five-finger hand position. As you progress you will have to read music that changes hand position. Often the fingering is given, but you will need to develop a feeling for the best time to change position – otherwise you'll simply run out of fingers!

Often the changes are related to scale and arpeggio patterns – this is another reason why it's important to know your scales! You'll find lots of fun scale practice in this volume's sister book *Improve your scales!* Grade 3.

Look at the next phrase – it moves out of the C major five-finger position. Can you see the best place to move hand position? Think about the fingering you use in a C major scale.

Here's the solution – you probably worked it out! You will put a 1st finger on the F – just as in playing a C major scale.

Sometimes there may be more than one fingering to choose from, depending on the melodic pattern. Have a look at this tune and think about which finger is best to put on the F♯ at the start of the second phrase.

The best solution is to put a 3rd finger on the F♯ (though a 4th would also work).

Most of the examples in this book change hand position. Always be on the look-out for where your hand position will move and you'll never run out of fingers!

Melodic exercises

Though the fingering is marked to help you, think carefully about
the hand position changes before you begin each exercise.

Prepared pieces

1 What is the key of this piece? Play the scale (or microscale*) and arpeggio.

2 What do you notice about the melodic pattern in bars 3 to 6?

3 What will you count? Tap the rhythm of each hand separately. Now tap the rhythms of both hands together.

4 Look through the piece for changes of hand position.

5 What is the musical significance of the *dim.*?

6 How will you put character into the music?

1 What is the key of this piece? Play the scale (or microscale*) and arpeggio.

2 Can you spot any repeated patterns – rhythmic or melodic?

3 What will you count? Tap the rhythm of each hand separately. Now tap the rhythms of both hands together.

4 Play the first note in each hand and try to hear the piece in your head.

5 Notice the one change of hand position.

6 How will you put character into the music?

* See page 40 for details.

Going solo!

Don't forget to prepare each piece carefully before you play it.

Stage 2

As well as single-note melodic lines you will also come across chords
– two or more notes played together. Here are some examples:

Seconds:

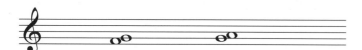 

Thirds:

Fourths:

Fifths:

Triads (made up of the first three notes of an arpeggio):

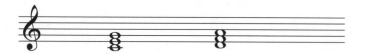 

Practise these chord shapes in different keys.

Write down some of your own favourite chords:

Melodic exercises

Prepared pieces

> **1** What is the key of this piece? Play the scale. Which fingers will you use for the chord at the start of the right-hand part?
>
> **2** Which notes are affected by the key signature?
>
> **3** Can you spot any repeated patterns – melodic or rhythmic? Are there are any scale patterns?
>
> **4** What will you count? Tap the rhythm of each hand separately. Now tap the rhythms of both hands together.
>
> **5** How will you finger the last four bars of the right hand? Why?
>
> **6** How will you give an expressive performance?

> **1** What is the key of this piece? Play the scale. How will you finger the chord in the first bar of the left hand? Where does this chord appear again?
>
> **2** Which notes are affected by the key signature?
>
> **3** What will you count? Tap the rhythm of each hand separately. Now tap the rhythms of both hands together.
>
> **4** What is the connection between the right and left-hand notes in bar 1?
>
> **5** Play the first notes in each hand and try to hear the piece in your head.
>
> **6** What ingredients give you clues to the character of this music?

Going solo!

Stage 3

A major

Rhythmic exercises

Remember to count two bars before you begin each exercise –
one out loud and one silently.

Melodic exercises

And don't forget to count two bars before you begin each melodic exercise as well!

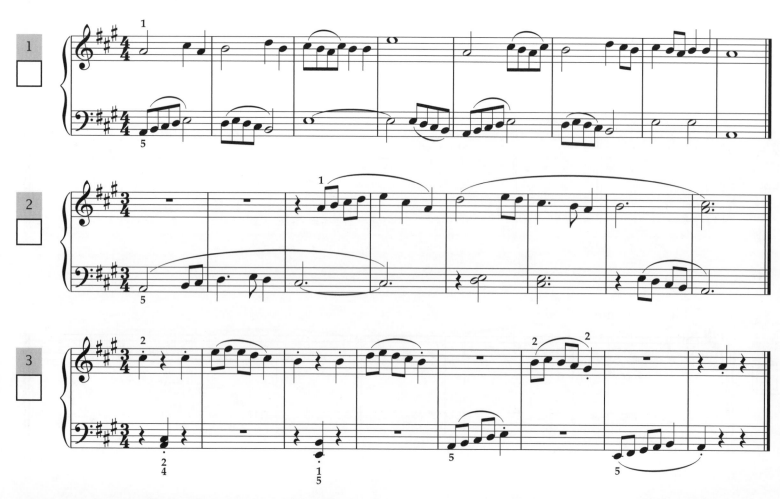

Prepared pieces

1 What is the key of this piece? Play the scale.

2 Look through the piece for changes of hand position.

3 What will you count? Tap the rhythm of each hand separately. Now tap the rhythms of both hands together.

4 Which chord do the final two notes of the right-hand part belong to?

5 Can you spot any scale or arpeggio patterns?

6 How will you put character into this piece?

1 What is the key of this piece? Play the scale.

2 Is the melody always in the right hand?

3 What will you count? Tap the rhythm of each hand separately. Now tap the rhythms of both hands together.

4 Look through the piece for changes of hand position.

5 Can you spot any scale or arpeggio patterns?

6 How will you put character into this piece?

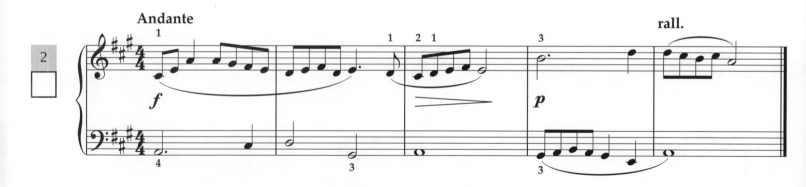

Going solo!

Don't forget to prepare each piece carefully before you play it.

Stage 4

Rhythmic exercises

Remember to count two bars before you begin each exercise –
one out loud and one silently.

Melodic exercises

What is the connection between B minor and D major? What will help you
decide which of the exercises is in B minor and which is in D major?

Prepared pieces

1 What is the key of this piece? Play the scale and arpeggio.

2 Can you spot any repeated patterns – rhythmic or melodic? Can you spot any scale patterns?

3 To which chord do the three notes of the first beat of the piece belong?

4 What will you count? Tap the rhythm of each hand separately then both together.

5 Try to hear the piece in your head and include the dynamic markings.

6 What character will you try to convey?

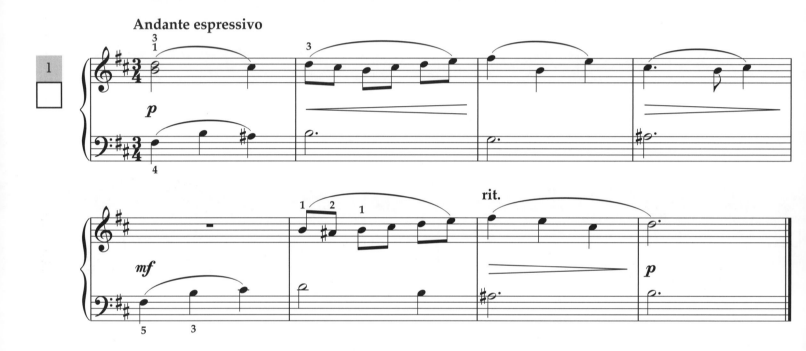

1 Play the scale and arpeggio of the key.

2 To which chord do all the notes in the first bar belong?

3 What will you count? Tap the rhythm of each hand separately. Now tap the rhythms of both hands together. Hear the rhythms of both hands in your head.

4 Does either hand change position in this piece?

5 What does *rit.* (bar 5) mean?

6 How will you give the piece character?

Going solo!

Stage 5

Rhythmic exercises

Remember to count two bars before you begin each exercise –
one out loud and one silently.

Melodic exercises

How are B♭ major and G minor connected?

Paul Harris's Exam Workout!

IMPROVE YOUR SIGHT-READING!

The ability to sight-read fluently is an important part of musical training, whether intending to play professionally, or simply for enjoyment. By becoming a good sight-reader, the player will be able to learn pieces more quickly, pianists will accompany more easily and all musicians will play duets and chamber music with confidence and assurance. Also, in grade examinations, a good performance in the sight-reading test will result in useful extra marks!

Improve your sight-reading! is a series of workbooks designed to help incorporate sight-reading regularly into practice and lessons, and to help prepare for the sight-reading test in grade examinations. It offers a progressive series of enjoyable and stimulating stages which, with careful work, should result in considerable improvement from week to week.

Step by step, the player is encouraged to build up a complete picture of each piece. Rhythmic exercises help develop and maintain a steady beat, whilst melodic exercises assist in the recognition of melodic shapes at a glance. The study of a prepared piece with associated questions for the student to answer helps consolidate acquired skills and, finally, the real, unprepared sight-reading test itself. Mark-boxes for each stage help keep a check on progress.

Such practical and methodical material is guaranteed to take the horror out of sight-reading!

0-571-53300-0	Piano Pre-Grade 1	NEW EDITION
0-571-53301-9	Piano Grade 1	NEW EDITION
0-571-53302-7	Piano Grade 2	NEW EDITION
0-571-53303-5	Piano Grade 3	NEW EDITION
0-571-53304-3	Piano Grade 4	NEW EDITION
0-571-53305-1	Piano Grade 5	NEW EDITION
0-571-53306-X	Piano Grade 6	NEW EDITION
0-571-53307-8	Piano Grade 7	NEW EDITION
0-571-53308-6	Piano Grade 8	NEW EDITION
0-571-51385-9	Violin Grade 1	
0-571-51386-7	Violin Grade 2	
0-571-51387-5	Violin Grade 3	
0-571-51388-3	Violin Grade 4	
0-571-51389-1	Violin Grade 5	
0-571-51735-8	Violin Grade 6	
0-571-51736-6	Violin Grade 7–8	
0-571-51075-2	Viola Grades 1–5	

0-571-51873-7	Cello Grades 1–3
0-571-51874-5	Cello Grades 4–5
0-571-51149-X	Double Bass Grades 1–5
0-571-51373-5	Descant Recorder Grades 1–3
0-571-51466-9	Flute Grades 1–3
0-571-51467-7	Flute Grades 4–5
0-571-51789-7	Flute Grade 6
0-571-51790-0	Flute Grades 7–8
0-571-51464-2	Clarinet Grades 1–3
0-571-51465-0	Clarinet Grades 4–5
0-571-51787-0	Clarinet Grade 6
0-571-51788-9	Clarinet Grades 7–8
0-571-51635-1	Saxophone Grades 1–3
0-571-51636-X	Saxophone Grades 4–5
0-571-51633-5	Oboe Grades 1–3
0-571-57021-6	Oboe Grades 4–5
0-571-51148-1	Bassoon Grades 1–5
0-571-51076-0	Horn Grades 1–5
0-571-50989-4	Trumpet Grades 1–5
0-571-51152-X	Trumpet Grades 5–8
0-571-56860-2	Trombone Grades 1–5

IMPROVE YOUR AURAL!

The very thought of aural, especially in examinations, strikes fear into the heart of many young pianists and instrumentalists. But aural should not be an occasional optional extra – it's something to be developing all the time, because having a good ear will help improve musicianship more than any other single musical skill.

Improve your aural! is designed to take the fear out of aural. Through fun listening activities, boxes to fill in and practice exercises, these workbooks and CDs focus on all the elements of the ABRSM aural tests. Because all aspects of musical training are of course connected, the student will also be singing, clapping, playing their instrument, writing music down, improvising and composing – as well as developing that vital ability to do well at the aural test in your grade exams!

0-571-53438-4	Grade 1 (with CD)	NEW EDITION
0-571-53439-2	Grade 2 (with CD)	NEW EDITION
0-571-53544-5	Grade 3 (with CD)	NEW EDITION
0-571-53545-3	Grade 4 (with CD)	NEW EDITION
0-571-53546-1	Grade 5 (with CD)	NEW EDITION
0-571-53440-6	Grade 6 (with CD)	NEW EDITION
0-571-53441-4	Grades 7–8 (with CD)	NEW EDITION

IMPROVE YOUR PRACTICE!

Improve your practice! is the essential companion for pianists, encapsulating Paul Harris's failsafe approach to learning.

With boxes for filling in, make-your-own playing cards, a handy practice diary and, when needed, an exam countdown, these books help to explore the pieces and to understand their character. The books will enable the student to develop ways of getting the most out of their practice sessions – whatever their length.

Most importantly, the wider musical skills such as aural, theory, sight-reading, improvisation and composition develop alongside, resulting in a more intelligent and all-round musician. Practice makes perfect!

0-571-52844-9	Piano Beginners
0-571-52261-0	Piano Grade 1
0-571-52262-9	Piano Grade 2
0-571-52263-7	Piano Grade 3
0-571-52264-5	Piano Grade 4
0-571-52265-3	Piano Grade 5
0-571-52271-8	Instrumental Grade 1
0-571-52272-6	Instrumental Grade 2
0-571-52273-4	Instrumental Grade 3
0-571-52274-2	Instrumental Grade 4
0-571-52275-0	Instrumental Grade 5

IMPROVE YOUR TEACHING!

Energising and inspirational, **Improve your teaching!** and **Teaching Beginners** are 'must have' handbooks for all instrumental and singing teachers. Packed full of comprehensive advice and practical strategies, they offer creative yet accessible solutions to the challenges faced in music education.

These insightful volumes are distilled from years of personal experience and research. In his approachable style, Paul Harris outlines his innovative strategy of 'simultaneous learning' as well as offering advice on lesson preparation, aural and memory work, effective practice and more.

0-571-52534-2	Improve your teaching!
0-571-53175-X	Improve your teaching! Teaching beginners
0-571-53319-1	Group Music Teaching in Practice (with ECD)

IMPROVE YOUR SCALES!

Paul Harris's **Improve your scales!** is the only way to learn scales.

The purpose of the workbooks is to incorporate regular scale playing into lessons and daily practice, and to help pupils prepare for grade examinations. Each volume contains all the scales, arpeggios and ranges required for the relevant Associated Board exam, along with complementary practical material. 'Know your notes!' makes sure the actual notes *are* known!; 'finger fitness' exercises strengthen fingers and cover technically tricky areas and the scales, arpeggios and broken chord study pieces place the material in a more musical context. Simple improvisations and even an opportunity to 'have a go' at composing a short tune encourage thought 'in the key'.

This unique approach encourages the student to understand and play comfortably within in a key, thus helping them pick up those valuable extra marks in exams, as well as promoting a solid basis for the learning of repertoire and for sight-reading.

0-571-53411-2	Piano Grade 1	NEW EDITION
0-571-53412-0	Piano Grade 2	NEW EDITION
0-571-53413-9	Piano Grade 3	NEW EDITION
0-571-53414-7	Piano Grade 4	NEW EDITION
0-571-53415-5	Piano Grade 5	NEW EDITION
0-571-51664-5	Violin Grade 3	
0-571-51665-3	Violin Grade 4	
0-571-51666-1	Violin Grade 5	
0-571-51663-7	Violin Grades 1–2	
0-571-52024-3	Flute Grades 1–3	
0-571-52025-1	Flute Grades 4–5	
0-571-51475-8	Clarinet Grades 1–3	
0-571-51476-6	Clarinet Grades 4–5	

Faber Music Limited

Burnt Mill, Elizabeth Way, Harlow, Essex CM20 2HX. Tel: +44 (0)1279 828982 Fax: +44 (0)1279 828983
www.fabermusic.com

Prepared pieces

1 What is the key of this piece? Play the scale. Which fingers will you use for the chords at the end of the right-hand part?

2 Which notes are affected by the key signature?

3 Which bars have the same rhythm in both hands? Are there any scale patterns?

4 What will you count? Tap the rhythm of each hand separately. Now tap the rhythms of both hands together.

5 Play the first note of each hand and then hear the piece through in your head.

6 How will you give a graceful performance?

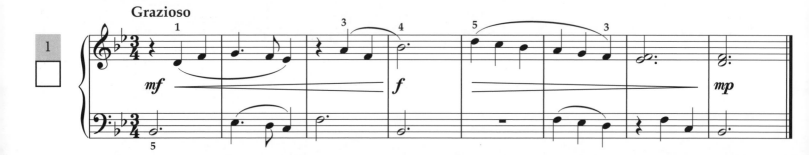

1 What is the key of this piece? Play the scale.

2 Can you see any scale patterns?

3 Are there any E♭s?

4 Does either hand move out of a five-finger position?

5 Now play the first notes in each hand and try to hear the piece in your head.

6 How will you bring this piece to life?

Going solo!

Don't forget to prepare each piece carefully before you play it.

Stage 6

E♭ major

Rhythmic exercises

Always count two bars before you begin each exercise –
one out loud and one silently.

Melodic exercises

And don't forget to count two bars before you begin each melodic exercise as well...

Prepared pieces

1 What is the key of this piece? Play the scale.

2 Which notes are affected by the key signature?

3 Which bars have the same rhythm in both hands? Are there any scale patterns?

4 What will you count? Tap the rhythm of each hand separately. Now tap the rhythms of both hands together.

5 Play the first note of each hand and then hear the piece through in your head.

6 How will you give a characterful performance?

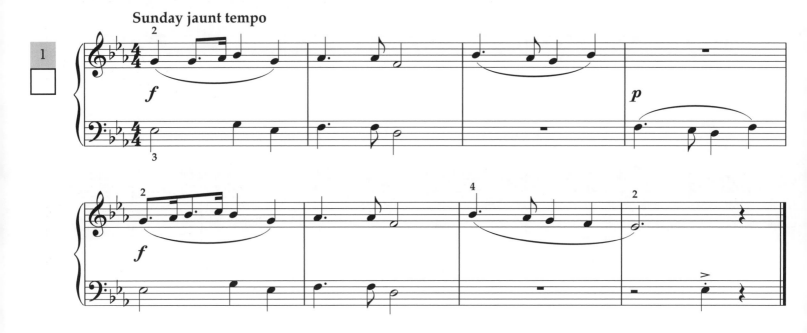

1 Play the scale and arpeggio of the key.

2 Which notes are affected by the key signature?

3 Is the melody mainly in the right or left hand?

4 What will you count? Tap the rhythm of each hand separately. Now tap the rhythms of both hands together.

5 Play the first note of each hand and then hear the piece through in your head.

6 How will you give your performance character?

Going solo!

Stage 7

$\frac{3}{8}$

Rhythmic exercises

Always count two bars before you begin each exercise – one out loud
and one silently – then continue to feel the pulse strongly.

Melodic exercises

Don't forget to count two bars before you begin each melodic exercise as well.

Prepared pieces

1 What is the key of this piece? Play the scale and arpeggio. How are the two pieces
  on this page related?

2 Can you describe the pattern formed by the right hand notes in bars 5, 6 and 7?

3 Study those three bars for a few moments, then play them from memory.

4 What will you count? Tap the rhythm of each hand separately. Now tap the rhythms
  of both hands together.

5 Can you spot any scale patterns?

6 What ingredients give you clues to the character of this piece?

1 What is the key of this piece? Play the scale and arpeggio. Which fingers will you
  use for the first note of each hand?

2 Where will you have to change hand position?

3 Which notes are affected by the key signature?

4 What will you count? Tap the rhythm of each hand separately. Now tap the rhythms
  of both hands together.

5 What pattern do the first two bars of the right-hand part form? Does this pattern
  occur again?

6 What ingredients give you clues to the character of this piece?

Going solo!

Don't forget to prepare each piece carefully before you play it.

Stage 8

Rhythmic exercises

Always count two bars before you begin each exercise – one out
loud and one silently – then continue to feel the pulse strongly.

Melodic exercises

Don't forget to count two bars before you begin each melodic exercise as well.

Prepared pieces

1 What is the key of this piece? Play the scale and arpeggio.

2 To which chord do the notes in left-hand bars 1 and 2 belong?

3 Does the left hand change position?

4 What will you count? Tap the rhythm of each hand separately. Now tap the rhythms of both hands together.

5 Can you spot any scale patterns?

6 Which ingredients give you clues to the character of this piece?

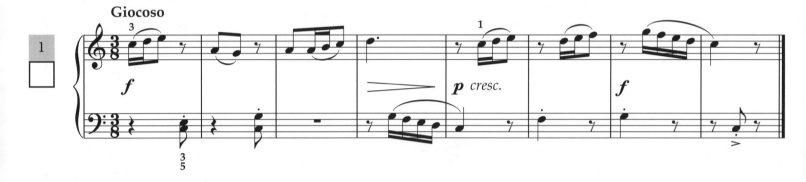

1 What is the key of this piece? Play the scale and arpeggio.

2 Where will you have to change hand position?

3 Which notes are affeccted by the key signature?

4 What will you count? Tap the rhythm of each hand separately. Now tap the rhythms of both hands together.

5 Compare the first left-hand bar with the first right-hand bar.

6 Play the first note of each hand and try to hear the piece in your head.

Going solo!

Stage 9

Rhythmic exercises

Melodic exercises

Prepared pieces

1 Are there any changes of position in the left-hand part?

2 Can you spot any repeated patterns – rhythmic or melodic?

3 What key is this piece in? Are there any scale patterns?

4 What do you notice about the rhythm in bar 4?

5 What will you count? Tap the rhythm of each hand separately. Now tap the rhythms of both hands together.

6 What ingredients give you clues to the character of this piece?

1 Look through the piece carefully and find your changes of hand position.

2 Can you spot any repeated patterns – rhythmic or melodic?

3 What key is the piece in? Can you spot any scale patterns?

4 Which interval is formed by the final two notes in the left hand?

5 What will you count? Tap the rhythm of each hand separately. Now tap the rhythms of both hands together.

6 What ingredients give you clues to the character of this piece?

Going solo!

Don't forget to prepare each piece carefully before you play it.

The golden rules

A sight-reading checklist

Before you begin to play a piece at sight, always consider the following:

1 Look at the time signature and decide how you will count the piece.

2 Look at the key signature and find the notes which need raising or lowering.

3 Notice patterns – especially those based on scales and arpeggios.

4 Check the fingering and hand position for the first notes of each hand.

5 Notice any markings that will help you convey the character.

6 Count at least one bar in.

When performing your sight-reading piece

1 Keep feeling the pulse.

2 Keep going at a steady tempo.

3 Ignore mistakes.

4 Look ahead – at least to the next note.

5 Keep your hands in position on the keyboard.

6 Play musically, always trying to convey the character of the music.

Look at each piece for about 30 seconds and try to feel that you are understanding what you see (just like reading these words).

Don't begin until you think you are able to play the piece accurately.

Microscales

If you don't know the whole scale, just the first five notes or even just the first three notes will do! Both patterns will give a good feel of the key.